Spring

Adult Coloring Book

Alisa Calder

First edition: 2017

This book belongs to:

SPRING

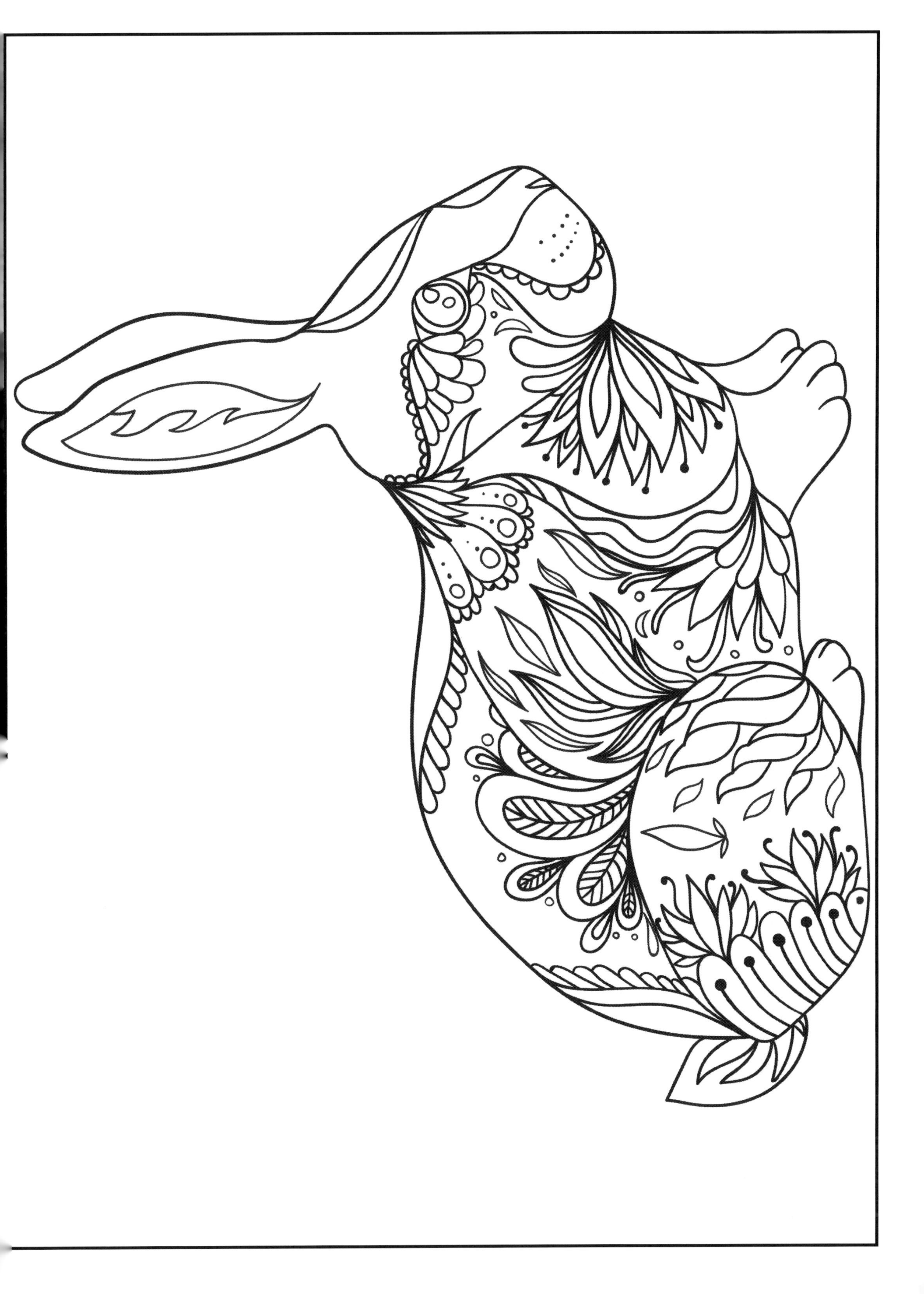

Thank you for purchasing this coloring book! I hope that you enjoy coloring it as much as I enjoyed creating it. Please consider leaving a review, I really appreciate hearing your opinion!

Sign-Up to Get a Free Coloring Book

Subscribe to our newsletter and get a free printable coloring book of some of our most popular illustrations. Plus you'll receive special offers, sneak peeks at new releases, and more. Visit us at **www.creativecoloring.co** for details.

We want to hear from you!

We hope you've enjoyed this coloring book and that is brings you many hours of fun, stress relief, and creativity. We'd love to see and share your creations.

Send us your ideas, suggestions, and finished artwork:

www.creativecoloring.co
facebook.com/creativecoloringpress
Instagram: @creativecoloringpress
Twitter: @creativecoloringpress

Bonus

Turn the page for bonus pages from some of our most popular coloring books.

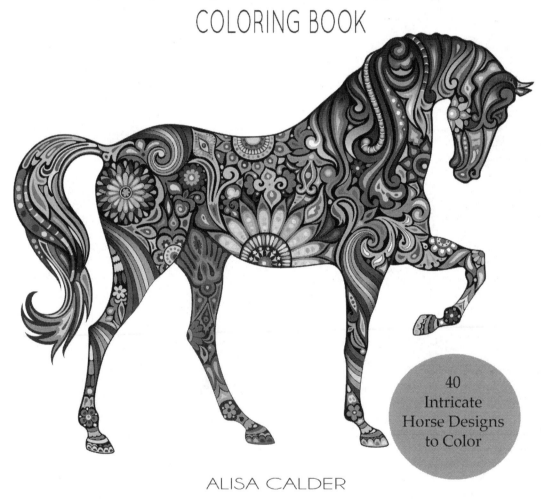

I'D AGREE WITH YOU BUT THEN WE'D BOTH BE WRONG.

HOTEL

FOLLOW
YOUR
BLISS

Made in the USA
San Bernardino, CA
15 May 2020